WORLD'S FAVORITE

Intermediate Violin Pieces

CONTENTS

ZIGEUNERWEISEN

SARASATE

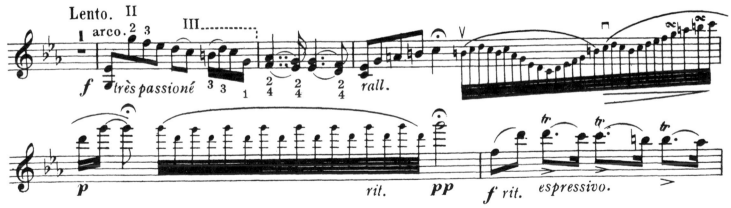

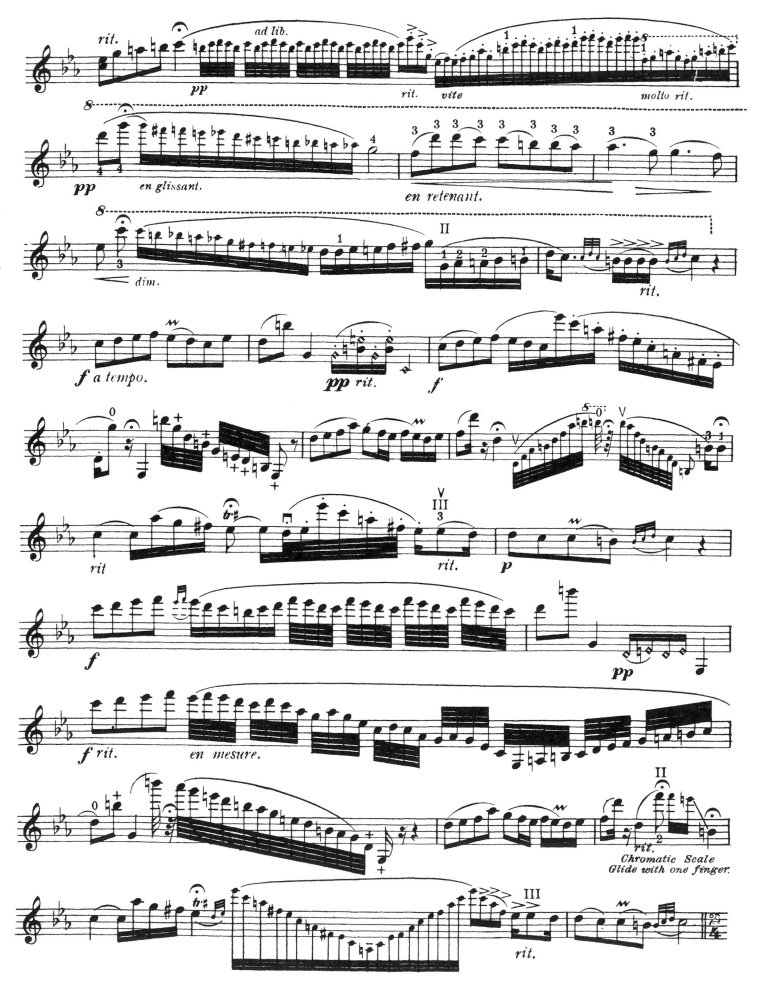

VIOLIN.

SERENADE

DRDLA

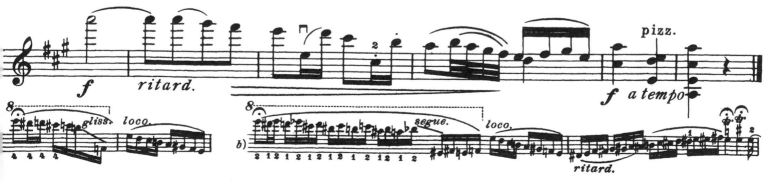

BERCEUSE

GODARD

Fine.

WALTZ
from "The Sleeping Beauty"

Tempo di Valse

Arranged by Maurice Lee

Violin

Violin

MINUET

BOCCHERINI

Tempo di Menuetto con un poco di moto

D.C. al Fine.

SERENADE

DRIGO

14

HUNGARIAN DANCE

No. 5

BRAHMS

Allegro appassionato
f
Sul G ad lib
mf
f
p leggiero
8va ad lib
f
marcato
p leggiero
ff double stops ad lib
marcato
mf
p un poco
rit.
fz a tempo
Vivace
f
8va
p poco rit
a tempo leggiero
poco rit
a tempo
p poco rit
a tempo leggiero
poco rit
a tempo
Allegro
f Sul G ad lib
8va ad lib
p leggiero
marcato
ff double stops ad lib
mf
p un poco rit
fz a tempo
ff

NOCTURNE in Db

(Original Key D♭)

CHOPIN

Arranged by Calvin Grooms

Lento sostenuto (♩.= 50)

17

VALSE BLUETTE

DRIGO

SANTA LUCIA

TRADITIONAL
Transcribed by
CALVIN GROOMS

POET AND PEASANT
Overture

von SUPPÉ

23

WALTZING DOLL

POLDINI
Arranged by Calvin Grooms

Tempo di Valse

TWO GUITARS

TRADITIONAL

27

IL TROVATORE

VERDI
Arranged by
SEP. WINNER.

Anvil Chorus

HUNGARIAN DANCE
No.6

Edited and revised by
MAURICE ARNOLD

BRAHMS

NOCTURNE
(G Minor)

CHOPIN
Arr. by A. WILHELMJ.

SERENADE

Arr. by M. HAUSER

SCHUBERT

Andantino Sentimentale

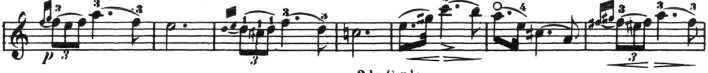

FLOWER SONG

LANGE

AVE MARIA

Molto adagio, religioso

F. SCHUBERT

ALLEGRO

FIOCCO

INTERMEZZO

HEINZ PROVOST

RUMANIAN RHAPSODY

Traditional
ENESCO - KAIL

SABRE DANCE

ARAM KHACHATURIAN
Arranged by R. Kail

42

TANGO

ALBENIZ

Andante grazioso

from "Thais"

MASSENET

CZARDAS

KAIL

ON WINGS OF SONG

F. MENDELSSOHN